Antique Jade

Antique Jade

Oscar Luzzatto-Bilitz

Paul Hamlyn

LONDON · NEW YORK · SYDNEY · TORONTO

Translated by Francis Koval from the Italian original

Antiche Giade

© 1966 Fratelli Fabbri Editori, Milan

This edition © 1969
The Hamlyn Publishing Group Limited
Hamlyn House,
The Centre, Feltham,
Middlesex

Text filmset in Great Britain by Yendall & Co. Ltd,
London

Printed in Italy by Fratelli Fabbri Editori,
Milan

In the minds of Western peoples the very word 'jade' tends to evoke fascinating images of the fabulous Orient. Strangely enough, the word has in reality a somewhat pedestrian European origin.

As far back as the 14th century, Marco Polo, returning to Europe from his travels, told of the vast numbers of trinkets and ornamental objects which he had observed at the court of the 'Great Chan' in China. He described these objects as being most skilfully carved from some extremely hard stone which was pleasing to the eye because of the variety and delicate loveliness of its colourings. Here then was probably the first European knowledge of jade. Without doubt, however, the first to import jade to Europe were the enterprising Portuguese sailors and merchants who established regular commercial relations with China in the 16th century.

In fact, on their arrival in Canton in 1517 the Portuguese caravels under the command of Fernào Peres de Andrade were received by the local population with great cordiality, though some time later the brother of Fernào, in command of other vessels, provoked ill-feeling because of his overbearing conduct and the acts of piracy he committed against peaceful Chinese merchants. Even so, forty years later Portugal was given the right to purchase a tiny peninsula at the mouth of the Canton River. It was here that the Portuguese built Macao, the first bridge-head for commercial exchanges between China and Europe, which rapidly developed into a prosperous settlement. The export of jade objects was then conducted in secrecy and was not devoid of danger. Not only was jade considered by the Chinese an article of exceptional value (even more precious than gold); they also attributed to the mysterious stone some qualities of a magical and curative nature. Hence the strict prohibition of its export.

Since time immemorial jade had been one of the main articles offered annually as a tribute to the Emperor of China by 'barbarian' princes of the borderlands in an endeavour to ensure his protection in case of conflict with neighbouring tribes, or simply as an object of barter for which silk was obtainable.

The attraction that jade has exercised through the ages has obviously been due to its exceptional hardness, which makes it impervious to damage although very difficult to work. On the other hand, its fascination derives from its subdued smooth brilliance which—according to the prevailing colours—can be redolent of the deep waters of a mountain lake or of the mistiness of a distant summit.

The same Chinese character 'Yü' that stands for 'jade' has also the meaning of 'jewel' or 'treasure'. Moreover, the stone has always been credited with

3.

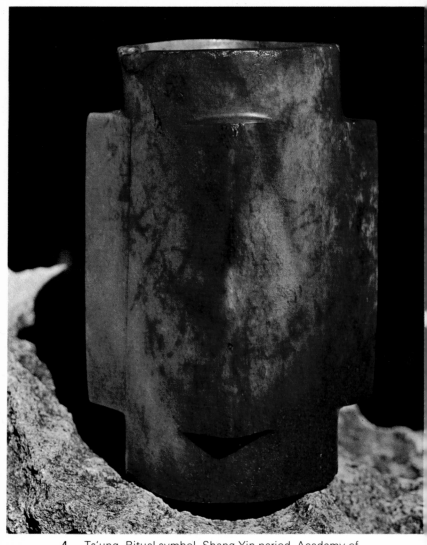

4. Ts'ung. Ritual symbol. Shang Yin period. Academy of Arts, Honolulu.

of jade was executed by hand with the help of a bone or bamboo stick, while the surface of the stone was covered with greasy ointment mixed with abrasive powder made from crushed garnets. Round holes were bored with a tubular tool made from an animal bone or a bamboo stick cut at a slant and sharpened with stones. This tube was made to rotate by means of a string wound round it and kept taut by a wooden bow. The to-and-fro movement of the little bow kept the hollow tube turning while pressure ensured close contact with the grease that contained the abrasive powder.

This primitive drill has probably some similarity to tools used in more recent times, and of which literary descriptions exist: a hollow cylinder made of bone or bamboo stem, turning on a smooth vertical pivot and kept rigid at the top by a wooden framework.

With the emergence of bronze implements in the 15th century BC and then of iron tools almost a thousand years later, the bamboo sticks were of course replaced by metal tubes. The general method of work, however, remained unaltered; and so it is easy to imagine how agonisingly slow the process was.

Still, in ancient records dating back to times in which such documents were usually adorned with fantastic legends, time and again reference is made to a wonder-knife called 'K'un Wu' which allegedly cut through jade as if it were chalk. The persistent repetition of such references leads us to believe—even allowing for the typically Chinese tendency to exaggerate—that there must be some truth in these statements and that in the distant past there indeed existed a more efficient tool than a pointed rod, even of metal. It would be logical to deduce that this might have been an iron tool with a diamond or corundum tip firmly embedded at one end.

According to legend, Yü the Great, the founder of the first Chinese Hsia Dynasty (towards the end of the 3rd millennium), was already in possession of one of these marvellous instruments. This seems absolutely impossible, since it is inconceivable that a diamond tip could be embedded in anything but a metal socket. But copper, the very first metal discovered by the Chinese (and by other peoples too) appeared in China only towards the middle of the 2nd millennium. An occasional import of that metal from the Near East, where it was in use before, is highly improbable since it is not borne out by archaeological findings or mentioned in traditional records.

A passage translated by Laufer from an ancient text brings up the subject in connection with Mu Wang, the fifth king of the Chou Dynasty, a character surrounded in Chinese literature by a galaxy of strange legends. When this ruler conducted an expedition at the head of his army to establish contact with some alien tribes inhabiting the frontier regions of his kingdom, it is reported that he received in homage from the ruler of these tribes a knife 'K'un Wu'. This report seems all the more credible in that the tribes, known as Jun, had in their territory vast deposits of iron ore and might have started quarrying from the 10th century BC onwards—a period roughly corresponding to the reign of Mu Wang. At any rate, if this instrument did in fact exist in such a remote period (which is by no means proved by archaeological finds), it must have been an object of exceptional value and surely not in general use. As a matter of fact, all the legends or early records mentioning such a 'wonder knife', refer to it only as the property of a sovereign ruler.

Even admitting the knowledge and use in those times of metal tools with diamond or corundum tips, it must be understood that this was a purely Chinese invention. If the Jun tribes were involved at all, their participation must have been limited to the supply of the metal part—since they only exported jade pebbles in their rough form, and there is no indication that they attempted to carve them. Hence the theory that they might have invented a carving tool for the shaping of jade seems somewhat absurd.

Laufer, who fifty years ago wrote the first European book on Chinese jades (and quite an exhaustive one at that), is of the opinion that the Chinese used diamond tips for jade-carving from the 1st millennium BC. Although his book is still considered authoritative today, his assertion in this respect is based on his own translation of the word 'chin-kang', which is frequently associated in legends with the knife 'K'un Wu', and associated in Europe with what we know as 'diamond'. He neglected to consider a variety of other meanings attached to the very same Chinese character, which is also used for the description of several particularly hard stones, among which

5. Pi disc in hatchet shape. Western Chou period. British Museum, London. Ex Eumorfopoulos Collection.

6. Strongly stylised human statuette. Late Chou or early Han period. British Museum, London. Ex Eumorfopoulos Collection.

7.

5.　　Pi disc in hatchet shape. Western Chou period (11th-8th centuries BC). British Museum, London. Ex Eumorfopoulos Collection. It symbolises perhaps the divine dualism Heaven-Earth, and is exceptional and unique. Dark-green nephritic jade with greyish and black veins.

6.　　Strongly stylised human statuette. Late Chou or early Han period (4th-2nd centuries BC). British Museum, London. Ex Eumorfopoulos Collection. A priest or judge. Grey-green nephritic jade with brown and black spots.

7.　　Hilt of a short ceremonial sword. Middle Chou period (9th-7th centuries BC). Museo Nazionale Orientale, Rome. Fiacchi-Gisondi Collection. Yellowish nephritic jade, strongly calcified. Even in archaic times jade was often used for handles or basket-hilts of short ceremonial swords which are typically Chinese.

8.　　Ts'ung. Ritual symbol. Probably Warring States (481-221 BC). Victoria and Albert Museum, London. Nephritic jade. This remarkable precision in the carving of the very hard stone is undoubtedly indicative of considerable technical progress, and suggests a later date than the Chou period diagnosed by English experts.

8. Ts'ung. Ritual symbol. Probably Warring States. Victoria and Albert Museum, London.

is the corundum. And the fact is that corundum, unlike diamonds, is normally found in China.

This ambiguity has probably come into being through the endeavour to keep the secrets of jade-carving in a few tradition-bound families who passed them on from father to son. Also the oily substance used, until fifty years or so ago, for the blending of the abrasive mixture figured prominently in strange tales obviously designed to draw a veil of secrecy over the whole procedure. Over the centuries it was always stressed in Chinese texts that the raw material, 'toad grease', was produced from toads killed in a special manner and in strictly defined circumstances. However, the grease in question has always been tallow from mutton or pork, melted and worked into a consistency similar to our own lard.

According to another popular misconception the 'toad grease' was supposed to soften the jade so that it could be cut more easily. Clearly, however high the viscosity of the ointment used, facility in carving hard stones by grinding them with metal implements (not to speak of bone or bamboo tools) depends not on the type of grease employed but on the quality of the abrasive powder.

To people unacquainted with Taoism and its complex mythology, this association of jade and toads may appear startling, since it establishes a strange connection between a precious stone of particular beauty and an animal that generally arouses repulsion among Western peoples. It must be remembered though that the Chinese peasants of ancient times were in no way prejudiced against the toad but, on the contrary, appreciated the little creature's ability to predict weather changes. Thus, in a primarily agricultural society it played an important part. Moreover, the toad figures in many Chinese legends.

One tells the story of Ch'ang Ho, the young and beautiful wife of a famous bowman of the legendary Emperor K'u. She was also called Hêng, meaning 'Crescent Moon'. Once during a sleepless night while she was watching the moon, an eclipse set in. Whereupon she took from the bedside her husband's mighty bow and saved the moon by shooting an arrow into the dark shadow that threatened it. Then she stole from her husband the jar containing the Elixir of Eternal Life (which was the Emperor's present to him for services rendered) and fled to the moon, where she was instantly changed into a toad. In this shape she lived in a magnificent palace in the sole company of the Jade Hare (Yü-t'u), who crushed beautiful jade into powder to make the Elixir of Eternal Life.

It is fairly certain that in the period between the 5th and the 1st centuries BC corundum or diamond tips were already used in drills which were still rudimentary, but developed to the extent that their rotation was ensured by pedal work, leaving the hands free. With simple metal implements it would have been impossible to produce the refined engravings typical of the period and the bracelets made of elaborately interlaced links carved out of one and the same block of jade. Infinite patience and superb craftsmanship were needed in order to carve these marvellous works of art with only the help of the primitive tools available. That is why the completed works aroused admiration bordering on awe and reverence, and why they fully deserved the name bestowed upon them which in literal translation means 'Works of Spirits'.

This method of work was extremely costly too, and not only because of the high value of the rough diamonds used for the drilling tips. One of the difficulties was that in those times no drill with interchangeable heads existed. Once the precious stone was firmly embedded at the end of the iron rod (which was in itself a difficult enough task), it was subject to rapid wear or it splintered, rendering the whole implement useless.

This technique must have been abandoned at the beginning of the Christian Era. It was revived in 18th-century China, but only for the purpose of engraving dedicatory poems and inscriptions in wonderfully minute and perfect characters, a task that could not be accomplished by any other means. This explains the almost complete absence in the intervening period of graphic indications which might have facilitated the exact dating of antique jade.

THE ORIGIN OF THE JADE USED IN CHINA

It is reasonable to assume that until the 10th or 11th century BC the only source of jade was in the alluvial deposits of Turkestan, which means that the pebbles or stones in question were never very big. True, ancient records mention a legendary Emperor who had a flight of steps built of white jade so that he could reach the abode of his favourite mistress with dignity. It must be remembered, however, that the Chinese word 'Yü', used for jade, easily led to confusion since it also denoted the kind of Parian marble quarried in China. This was a comparatively rare

9. Ts'ung. Ritual symbol. Middle Chou period. British Museum, London. Ex Eumorfopoulos Collection.

mineral, used as a rule for the temples or palaces of sovereign rulers. Even there it was not used for the construction of the whole building (as the Chinese always preferred timber to stone) but simply for outside stairs or for bridges which linked islands in artificial lakes, and so on.

One more proof of the confusion caused by the use of the ambiguous term 'Yü' is supplied by the Chinese pharmacopoeia, which prescribed the oral

10. Basket-hilt of a short ceremonial sword. Warring States. Museo Nazionale Orientale, Rome. Fiacchi-Gisondi Collection.

9.   Ts'ung. Ritual symbol. Middle Chou period (9th-7th centuries BC). British Museum, London. Ex Eumorfopoulos Collection. Yellow nephritic jade with brown stripes. The flattened shape and certain irregularities in the central ribbing as well as in the incisions at the corners are fairly trustworthy clues to the object's date of origin.

10.   Basket-hilt of a short ceremonial sword. Warring States (481-221 BC). Museo Nazionale Orientale, Rome. Fiacchi-Gisondi Collection. Off-white nephritic jade. The symmetrical and semi-geometrical decoration is typical of the period. Origin: Honan.

11.   Chisels. Chou period (1122-256 BC). Museo Nazionale Orientale, Rome. Fiacchi-Gisondi Collection. Yellow nephritic jade. Complete absence of decoration makes the establishment of a more exact date impossible. Nevertheless, the shaped top of the smaller chisel (on the right in the reproduction) suggests that it is of a later date than the other, i.e. from the period between the 5th and the 3rd centuries BC. The other chisel could date back to the early Chou (11th-9th centuries BC).

12.   Ritual Pi disc. Warring States (481-221 BC). W. Rockhill Nelson Gallery of Art, Kansas City. Off-white nephritic jade with green veins. The exquisitely carved ornaments, consisting mainly of two mythical lions on the outside and one even more stylised on the inside, combine to create a work of singular beauty. There is some similarity to the specimen presented by the Chinese Government in 1935-1936 at the First Exhibition of Chinese Art in London.

11.

administration of pulverised jade for various ailments. Now there is no doubt whatsoever that genuine jade could not be assimilated by the human organism without causing serious illness or even death. Hence the deduction that the substance employed as medicine must have been powder of marble or magnesite, minerals which in their natural state have a consistency that is hard enough to be mistaken for jade but which are soluble in the gastric juices and capable of relieving excess acidity.

The first reliable reports of the extraction of jade from rock in Khotan date back to the 12th century. It is fairly certain, in fact, that very large blocks of jade were being carved then for the Emperors of the Yüan and Ming Dynasties, as well as for the Ch'ing, their successors. The most famous block, uniformly white, was shaped about the year 1410 into a pillar approximately six feet high; on it, for the benefit of posterity, the Emperor Yung Lo allegedly inscribed one of his long poems with his own hand. This exceptional piece of work is said to have been placed originally in the Imperial Palace in Peking, but it seems to have disappeared. As in the case of several big mountain-shaped jades kept in the same place, there is little likelihood that it was carried away by Chiang K'ai-shek and taken on his forced march to the south. The very size and weight of these unique works of art would have prevented him from doing so. Some rumours, vague and difficult to verify, circulating during the last war hinted at the presence of the precious pillar in Japan.

In Turkestan—a region which in the course of history was in turn independent, a protectorate and a Chinese province—the quarrying of jade and its separation from the rock in which it was embedded has always been extremely difficult. Instead of using gunpowder, the quarry-men used to light big fires and keep them going in the immediate vicinity of a jade seam, so that the different rate of expansion caused by the heat in the actual seam and the surrounding ore produced cracks. Water was thrown on the strongly heated rock surface in order to enlarge these cracks, and then wedges of hardwood were driven into fissures with hammers. Such a procedure was not only very slow but also involved considerable wastage of the precious material.

The extraction of jade from the rockface did not, however, slow down the efforts to collect alluvial pebbles from riverbeds—a method still used today by riverside dwellers in some parts of Turkestan. Such tasks were generally assigned to women, who at the time of low water waded into the river, fished out the stones and threw them on to the banks, where men proceeded to segregate them. This custom of employing female labour for 'jade fishing' was dictated (like so many other peculiarities still prevailing in small localities in the interior) by a curious tradition of legendary origin. It was believed that the jade was intentionally hiding in the depths of the riverbed, emerging only in certain favourable circumstances, and that above all the precious mineral was susceptible to feminine attraction.

12. Ritual Pi disc. Warring States. W. Rockhill Nelson
Gallery of Art, Kansas City.

13. Pendant in dragon shape. Late Chou period. Museo
Nazionale Orientale, Rome. Fiacchi-Gisondi Collection.

13.   Pendant in dragon shape. Late Chou period. Museo Nazionale Orientale, Rome. Fiacchi-Gisondi Collection. White jade with brown speckles. The stylised serpentine shape of the object as well as the ornamental motif of spirals provides sufficient evidence for the date of origin: 5th-3rd centuries BC.

14.   Ritual Pi disc. Warring States (481-221 BC). W. Rockhill Nelson Gallery of Art, Kansas City. Green jade with brown spots (caused by iron impurities). The geometrical motif composed of exquisitely carved and highly stylised, intertwined dragons represents the culmination of jade-carving skill achieved by the ancient Chinese in this period. This masterpiece was certainly produced with the help of diamond drills.

15.   Pendant in stag shape. Late Chou period (4th-3rd centuries BC). Metropolitan Museum, New York. Rogers Fund. Off-white nephritic jade. The remarkable elegance with which the horns of the animal are shaped allows this object to be located to this period.

16.   Ancient safe-conducts. Middle Chou period (827-781 BC). Short cylinders made of brown jade, strongly calcified. From a drawing of the originals kept in a private collection in Peking.

15. Pendant in stag shape. Late Chou period.
Metropolitan Museum, New York. Rogers Fund.

16. Ancient safe-conducts. Middle Chou period.

Despite recent rumours to the contrary, it seems fairly certain that no jade is found in China proper. Since time immemorial it has always come from Turkestan, where the principal alluvial deposits exist in the rivers Yurungkash and Karakash, whose names in translation in fact signify 'River of Green Jade' and 'River of White Jade'. Both of them have their source in the mountain chain called K'un-lun.

A very ancient legend connected with Tao folk-lore seems to give poetic confirmation of the theory that jade was confined to the western regions. Once upon a time the 'Jade Queen' Hsi Wang Mu lived in her fabulous palace built on an inaccessible peak of the K'un-lun Mountains, attended by twelve princesses-in-waiting. Now, literally translated, Hsi Wang means 'Rulers of the West', and hence the whole name signifies the Queen (or Mother) of the Rulers of the West.

As a matter of fact, there exists, although histori-cally not clearly defined, a vague mention of a race that inhabited the Turkestan regions now called Khotan and Yarkand and which was governed by a woman.

The story continues with the description of a journey made in the 10th century BC by the Emperor Mu Wang of the Chou Dynasty, who owned eight bewitched stallions—which enabled him to cover in one night the whole length of his immense empire. The aim of this journey was to establish a relation-ship with the above mentioned 'Jade Queen'.

Since all the legends that pass from one century to

another possibly have a grain of truth in them, it is conceivable that this fable refers to an approach made by the Chinese sovereign to the western tribes with a view to obtaining a regular supply of jade. In those times Turkestan was, of course, independent and inhabited by a group known as the Jun.

The continuous interest in the jade country shown by the Chinese, and their wish to maintain friendly relations with its inhabitants, are somehow reflected in the continuation of the legend which deals with the love affairs of the mythical and immortal Queen Hsi Wang Mu.

About a thousand years after her affair with the Emperor Mu Wang of the Chou Dynasty, she fell in love with the Emperor Wu Ti of the Han Dynasty (156-87 BC). In order to meet him she descended from her palace, accompanied by five of her princesses— the latter being called 'Yü Nü', which in literal translation means 'Jade Girls'. In that period Turkestan, although semi-independent, belonged nominally to the great Han Empire; so this story may represent a poetic record of tribute-paying and submission by the Jun leaders to the Chinese Emperor. Wu Ti had become a fervent Tao supporter and believed in the Elixir of Eternal Life. It was from this period that the confusion regarding the qualities of jade existed. Jade was considered one of the Elixir's principal ingredients, and thus acquired an even higher value in the eyes of most Chinese people.

Towards the end of the 13th century Marco Polo, during his adventurous expedition to the mysterious

19.

Central-American jadeite seen in thin slices under the microscope presents a clearly crystalline structure, not a fibrous crypto-crystalline one like nephritic jade. Its greater transparency and shiny surface is in contrast to the muted brilliance of genuine jade.

Neither jade nor jadeite are subject to changes in their original state—that is to say when preserved from contact with air. Nevertheless, the slow process of oxygenation and carbonisation has caused obvious changes in the surface and in the structure of carved objects preserved in tombs or simply covered by earth. On the surface dull stains begin to appear and these tend to penetrate in depth. Of course, this pro-.cess—which is improperly called 'calcification' and should rather be described as progressive deterioration—is so slow that it only becomes noticeable in objects aged at least a thousand years. The appearance of such symptoms depends largely on the conditions of the locality concerned, particularly on the humidity and other properties of the soil.

It is obvious that even if in this way the beauty of an object may be affected, the deterioration—signifying the great age of the object—may increase its value, turning it into a 'collector's item'. In recent times, the increasing demand for antiques has encouraged unscrupulous dealers to attempt to produce fraudulent imitations. Modern copies of very ancient jade objects are being made and then heated in high-temperature furnaces so as to produce an opaque surface layer which can easily deceive the layman's eye.

In all probability, in the pre-Columbian period the ancient inhabitants of Central America used to quarry jade and jadeite from the rocks in the mountains of the Andes chains or in the Mexican Plateau. So far, no systematic research has been done to discover such mining localities.

More recently nephritic jade has been found sporadically in various parts of the world, and particularly in huge alluvial deposits in certain rivers of southern Siberia. This Siberian jade is generally dark-green, but with splashes of lighter green and blackish dots which are due to the presence of graphite in the composition of the mineral. In the language of the Chinese, its principal importers, this stone is called 'Spinach Jade'.

In a state of absolute purity both jade and jadeite should, in theory at least, be white. In reality, however, only jade, and not jadeite, is found in such a state, and not very often at that. White jade which is slightly translucent and opalescent is called by the Chinese 'Mutton-Fat Jade'. The wide range of colours found in nephritic jade is due to the presence in its composition of various metallic oxides or silicates. The most frequent colouring agent is iron. In the shape of ferrous oxide (magnetite) it endows the jade—according to the quantity present—with colouring that ranges from grey (most commonly encountered) to plain uniform black (very rare). Pale greyish-green shades ranging to near-black dark green at the other end of the scale, are due to the presence of ferrous silicate, which in very rare cases produces also a decisively blue shade. Ferric silicate, on the other hand, produces a colour that ranges from yellowish orange to dark brown. The highest value is attached to yellow jade when its colour is distinguished by clarity and uniformity.

The combined presence of different pigments leads to a great variety of colours and shades. Tiny traces of manganese produce the frequently found whitish

25.   Double belt-buckle. Han period (206 BC -AD 220). Private Collection, Milan. Ex Fiacchi-Gisondi Collection. Jade with black veins. Although the rudimentary carving on the clasp is the object's only decoration, the buckle is impressive in the elegance of its finish and the perfect fit of its two curved halves.

26.   Ritual Pi disc. Han period (206 BC- AD 220). Museo Nazionale Orientale, Rome. Fiacchi-Gisondi Collection. White, slightly translucent jade. The relief ornaments carved on the disc's circumference consist of eight classical 'trigrammes' (series of three lines—either intact or broken—in all possible combinations) which in their totality (Pa-Kua) represent the integrity of the Cosmic Universe.

27.   Pendant: serpent-like dragon. British Museum, London. Off-white nephritic jade. Although this specimen has been classified as dating back to the Six Dynasties period (AD 265-589), it is more likely to originate from the Sung period (AD 960-1279).

28.   Duck or other bird. T'ang period (AD 618-906). British Museum, London. Ex Eumorfopoulos Collection. Dark-brown nephritic jade with traces of varnish baked on natural red pigments.

(spade), with the usual central opening. It is my personal belief that it is a representation of Heaven-Earth dualism.

It must be remembered that for the ancient Chinese a separate and external earth cult did not exist. Earth was seen as the deity that regulated mankind's very existence. Next to the Sun god there was the Earth goddess, and their union was tantamount to the conception of Universe, the sole beginning of life.

27. Pendant: serpent-like dragon. Probably Sung period. British Museum, London.

In tombs discovered at Anyang, the last capital of the Shang Dynasty, various Pi's were found, embellished with engravings which range from simple semi-geometrical motifs to patterns repeating the complex symbol language of the ritual bronzes of the same era. This is an art which can hardly be called 'animalistic' because animals (or parts of animals) are represented in forms which are always unreal, fantastic and symmetrically formalised. The dominant figure, decorative and typically Chinese, is a monster associated in ancient mythology with the concept of rain or of water in general (its Chinese name is 'Kuei').

The myth of this Master of the Rains (or of the River) goes back to the dawn of history, although the name must have been coined in comparatively recent times (probably not before the 10th century AD). Parts of this dragon such as the tusks, claws and horns appear interlaced in a continuous zigzag pattern obviously shaped in accordance with a symbol language which has remained somewhat obscure to this day but which is not devoid of a peculiar fascination.

In the bronzes this art is, of course, much more refined and reaches its peak in the Shang period, approximately at the time when King P'an Keng transferred his capital to Anyang (in 1401 BC according to tradition, or in 1300 BC according to some modern historians). This move to the east was made in order to escape an attack launched by the Jun, the very race closely connected with the story of Chinese jade, since they were the chief suppliers. The name of the region in which the new capital was situated—the Yin Desert—was used by P'an Keng when he decided to change the name of his dynasty from Shang to Yin. This explains the seeming contradictions, likely to create a certain confusion among the less expert students of the subject, which occur in references made to this subject by modern historians.

The superiority of contemporary bronzes can be easily explained. These refined works of art were often produced with the cire perdu ('lost wax') technique. The use of this very soft material allowed for very subtle incisions with any kind of pointed tip, even a wooden one, whereas in the case of the extremely hard jade it was virtually impossible.

It is during this Shang period that a peculiar figure appears. Although it undoubtedly possesses a symbolic significance, its actual meaning is to this day a subject of controversy.

Its name is 'T'ao T'ieh', and it is a grotesque and crude mask with two big round eyes, but with the lower jaw missing. The large tusks rising from the upper jaw endow it with a ferocious and bestial appearance. From both sides of the nose sprout two inward-curving horns. A band usually runs under the eyes, rising upwards at right angles and ending in a tail. Under this band, on both sides of the jaw, crooked claws are visible. The most feasible theory concerning this mask is that it represents the head of a tiger with the lower jaw removed to enable a Shaman to slip it over his head for use in some unknown rite.

The etymology of the name 'T'ao T'ieh' is also uncertain: it appears unexpectedly in a few Chinese texts with a diversity of meanings. For example, in the *Chan hai king*, as translated by Legge and reported by Granet in his *Danses et Légendes*, it is a man-eating monster which lived on a mountain guarding rich copper mines.

These two forms—the Kuei and the T'ao T'ieh—are nearly always associated in such a way that the latter occupies a central position, while the two lateral Kuei appear as its continuation.

During the whole Shang period this representation (more rudimentary, of course, in the jade objects than in the bronzes) bears an expression of awe-inspiring ferocity. With advancing centuries this realism is mitigated and gradually superseded by more conventional stylisation. In the Pi's this kind of design is rather rare. In view of their annular shape, the decorative engravings for the most part display a continuous and regularly repeated pattern.

During the whole Western Chou period (in other words until the 7th century BC) the Shang style in carving shows a trend towards greater simplicity and becomes more primitive. Then follows the period historically known as that 'of the Springs and Autumns' (771-481 BC), a name derived from the famous *Annals* of the Lu State, the country of Confucius. According to brief records referring to the time between the 6th and 4th centuries BC it was then that implements with corundum or diamond tips came into use, as can be deduced from the greater refinement of jade engravings. This new technique reaches its culmination in the following period (482-221 BC), known as the era 'of the Warring States' due to the fact that the central government suffered a complete loss of power, so that China was devastated by continuous wars between vassal states. Strangely enough, the continuous state of war did not seem to affect the development of arts, and particularly not the art of jade carving. Not only are the jade objects of this period superbly engraved, but also openwork carving of exquisite perfection first appears.

While keeping their basic shape and the traditional religious symbols, the Pi's of this period change from simple ring-shaped discs into objects of rare artistic beauty. In Plate 12 we can admire the specimen kept in the Nelson Gallery (Kansas City), which resembles closely the Pi originally belonging to the Imperial Treasure and presented by the Chinese Government at the First London Exhibition in 1935-1936. Made of the seldom found yellow nephrite, it gives a good idea of the artistic refinement attained towards the end of the Chou period. Incorporated into the outer edge of the disc are two perfectly carved imaginary monsters. The annular body, on the other hand, displays a precise geometrical pattern of tiny buttons — which does not at first sight convey any idea of the exhausting work that went into carving this bas-relief out of jade that still presents a perfectly smooth and polished surface.

In my opinion this particular decorative pattern derives from the general concept of abundance and fertility, because these tiny protuberances can only represent grains of millet, the staple Chinese cereal of archaic times. Usually this kind of background decoration is called 'rice grain motif'; but such a definition seems erroneous because rice, now Asia's staple food, only reached China proper in comparatively recent times. In a predominantly agricultural civilisation the seed had probably assumed almost mystic significance, and the mystery of its transformation must have been associated with the religious Heaven-Earth dualism. As for the date of origin of the last-mentioned Pi, I should be inclined to conjecture the 5th-4th centuries BC.

A Pi in my own collection—which was found in a tomb of the Han period in southern Honan—appears at first sight completely dark brown and opaque. Holding it against the light, however, one discerns semi-transparent green areas whose colour is probably that of the original jade. And yet this state of deterioration and almost complete opacity cannot be taken as proof that the piece in question is of a more remote origin than the tomb itself. Its fairly well preserved geometrical decoration consists of small spirals which enclose a round protuberance. This is the more advanced symbol of fertility (in fact the seed and the germ that sprouts therefrom) which is found as a motif, both in carvings and in bronzes, as from the 3rd century BC and through the whole Han period.

This can be taken as a convincing demonstration of the fact that the degree of deterioration in jade is only a very general indication for determining its age.

28. Duck or other bird. T'ang period. British Museum, London. Ex Eumorfopoulos Collection.

In fact, the rate of deterioration varies greatly according to the conditions of the place where the object has been preserved, and cannot therefore serve on its own as a basis for pinpointing its date. Among the various examples quoted in this book cases may be observed in which very ancient objects show far less marked deterioration than others of lesser age. The same principle, incidentally, applies to bronzes.

Among the jade in the Manlio Fiacchi collection, donated to the National Museum of Oriental Art in Rome but not yet exhibited or catalogued, I have

32. Goat-like animal. T'ang period. Museo Nazionale Orientale, Rome. Fiacchi-Gisondi Collection.

Each of the four sides has a central vertical rib, and parallel incisions of alternating depth link horizontally the rib and the edge of each side. The Ts'ung is the symbol of the Earth deity.

No specimen of this kind has been found in Neolithic tombs. This is no doubt due to the extreme difficulty of perforating a cylinder of such size, and of working a big block of particularly hard stone with the primitive tools of the times. The various specimens found in the Shang tombs were defined as jade by the Chinese and accepted as such by museums in the West. It is my opinion, however, that at least all those of the pre-Anyang period (and also the

33. Crouching animal. T'ang period. Museo Poldi Pezzoli, Milan.

majority attributed to the Anyang period itself) are made not of jade but of a softer material which resembles marble.

The specimen which is now in the Honolulu Museum (Plate 4), and which has been reproduced from a photograph made on the Anyang excavation site, is probably the prototype of such objects carved in real jade. It is made of yellow nephrite with strongly marked reddish stains. Its rudimentary and somewhat coarse shape reveals the great difficulties that the ancient carver must have encountered. It has no indentations at the edges—these being a characteristic of all the other pieces found so far.

This fact discredits the theory of the probable origins of the Ts'ung advanced by Laufer. He starts from the notion that in the earliest ages the ancestral tablets of the monarchs, when not exhibited during ritual ceremonies, were kept in a tube protected by four slabs of jade which also had the purpose of preventing the tablets from rolling up. According to this theory the indentations at the edge of the square sides of a Ts'ung corresponded to the incisions made in the four rectangular tablets. This allowed a cord to be used to fix them in place, avoiding the risk of the cord slipping on the smooth cylinder. He does not contest the assumption that the Ts'ung represented the symbol of the Earth deity. The connection with the object's role as a receptacle for the archaic ancestral tablets had to be sought in the mythical origins of those reigning families which could be associated with the religious concept of Mother Earth.

33. Crouching animal. T'ang period (AD 618-906). Museo Poldi Pezzoli, Milan. Sculptured all round out of a yellow nephrite pebble with reddish specks. The caparison, sketchily incised on the animal's back, and the trunk-like snout (folded up against the body) suggest that the unknown Chinese artist might have intended to portray a resting elephant.

34. Goblet for festive occasions. Sung period (AD 960-1279). Victoria and Albert Museum, London. White jade with greenish-brown specks. The body,of the vessel is decorated with mythological animals in high-relief and in bas-relief. The handle is in the shape of a stylised dragon. Perhaps made in the first half of the 12th century.

35. Pendant in small hatchet shape. Sung period (AD 960-1279). Museo Nazionale Orientale, Rome. Fiacchi-Gisondi Collection. Yellowish jade. The top is sculptured in dragon shape, while the upper part is decorated with a strip of lightly carved archaic motifs.

36. Cylindrical bracelet. Sung period (AD 960-1279). Museo Nazionale Orientale, Rome. Fiacchi-Gisondi Collection. White-brown jade. On its outer side this bracelet shows ornaments carved in high-relief.

34.

35. Pendant in small hatchet shape. Sung period. Museo
Nazionale Orientale, Rome. Fiacchi-Gisondi Collection.

Similar notions can be found in some Chinese texts which Laufer no doubt translated and consulted. There is no point in enumerating all the various theories which try to explain the origins and raison d'être of this object's shape. Although they are always based on ingenious arguments by logical deduction, they can be taken as no more than personal opinions.

One fairly plausible hypothesis, however, seems worth mentioning. Some authors maintain that, to start with, the object in question was simply a cylindrical tube and—in the primitive Chinese mud huts without windows—served as a kind of air-funnel or little chimney. Such an introduction of life-giving air and humidity might have been considered metaphorically as an essential link between heaven and earth. Still, no trace of such a cylindrical Ts'ung has been found so far in archaeological excavations.

It is fairly certain that, at first, these objects were comparatively tall. This fact does not in any way affect the theory of their function as receptacles for ancestral tablets, which anyway in the course of time tended to be squashed, almost to the point of becoming annular in shape during the Chou period. It is worth repeating, however, that most of the archaic tall Ts'ung are probably not made of genuine jade, even though the Chinese classify them as 'Yü'.

Let us pass from these objects of symbolic significance to implements more widely used—although in view of their great value they were in ancient times predominantly used only in ritual ceremonies. Here then is a summary description of some weapons and cutting implements made of jade.

Just because the use of such objects was the prerogative of the more cultured classes (mainly potentates and priests) they very often represent artistic achievement at its highest. In view of jade's high degree of hardness it is not surprising that before the discovery of metals it was accepted as the most suitable material for the blades of knives and daggers. This tradition persisted well into the Bronze Age.

Archaeological finds prove that during the whole 2nd millennium human sacrifices were part of the common rites performed at funerals of important persons. In some tombs of the Shang Dynasty, dozens of skeletons were found in the central burial chamber around the dead king or prince. In accordance with an unknown ritual their skulls were aligned separately, all turned in the same direction. In one of these tombs a heavy jade axe was found with two holes in the thick side. That is where the wooden handle was fixed, but by now it had disintegrated into dust. There is little doubt that this was a beheading axe.

In this period the priests possessed great religious and political power, often greater than that of the sovereign. Therein lies the explanation for the exquisite artistry of ancient sacrificial knives, which were in all probability used exclusively by priests. The blade was usually of jade, with a bronze hilt

41.   Cylindrical bracelet. Sung period (AD 960-1279). Museo Nazionale Orientale, Rome. Fiacchi-Gisondi Collection. Multi-coloured jade. Although not common by any means, here is a typical example of the infinite combinations of colour which can appear in a single piece of jade because of various metallic impurities. On the outside the bracelet is decorated in high relief.

42.   Crescent-shaped plaque. Sung period (AD 960-1279). Musée Guimet, Paris. Green jade. The two ends of the crescent have the shape of dragon heads which face each other. Also noteworthy is the meticulously carved pattern of fish scales, certainly achieved only through infinite patience. A typical piece of the Sung period.

43.   Mythical monster, sculptured all round. Probably late Sung. Museo Poldi Pezzoli, Milan. White jade with brown veins. The somewhat rudimentary workmanship of this piece has little in common with the refinement of the 12th century. Hence the strong suspicion that it was made at the end of the Sung period (13th century).

44.   Big tortoise. Ming period (AD 1368-1644). British Museum, London. Grey-green nephrite (the 'cabbage jade' of the Chinese). This specimen's exceptional dimensions (52 centimetres) lead to the conclusion that during the Ming period the import of nephritic jade from Khotan into China was no longer confined to alluvial pebbles but included also huge blocks obtained from quarries. Certainly the beginnings of jade extraction from rocks date back to the 11th or 12th century.

41. Cylindrical bracelet. Sung period. Museo Nazionale
Orientale, Rome. Fiacchi-Gisondi Collection.

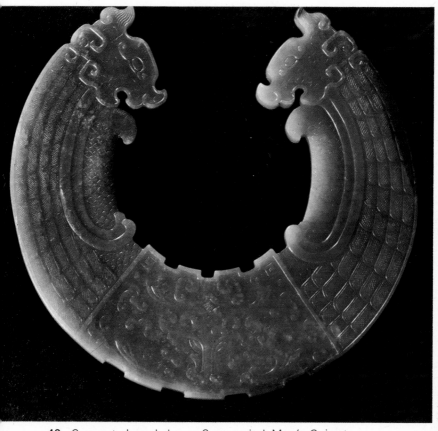

42. Crescent-shaped plaque. Sung period. Musée Guimet, Paris.

43. Mythical monster, sculptured all round. Probably late
Sung. Museo Poldi Pezzoli, Milan.

For the Chinese the concept of the soul has always been somewhat nebulous. The general belief was that at the moment of death the 'Superior Spirit' of an individual immediately fled the body in the direction of a not very well defined celestial limbo which was in a typically Chinese way described as the 'Yellow Sources'.

The official announcement of an Emperor's death, for instance, summed up the event thus: 'The Son of Heaven has descended to the Yellow Sources.' Western commentators interpret this expression as descending into the Underworld. This seems fairly exact considering the Latin meaning of 'Inferos'— Kingdom of the Dead, or of the Souls. For the Chinese, however, the Paradise-Hell dualism in its traditional sense has never existed. In my opinion, therefore, this is an allusion to a mythical kingdom situated in the mountains where the Yellow River (Hoang Ho) starts. This stream has all through the ages been identified with China's protective deity, playing somewhat the same role as the Nile in the time of the Pharaohs.

But apart from this 'Superior' or 'Celestial' Spirit which left the body immediately at the moment of death, it was believed that various other 'earthly' spirits existed which for the time being stayed behind in the dead body. These had to be appeased with offerings and delicately enjoined to depart—which was accomplished by complicated rites which could extend over several months, particularly if the deceased was rich. In the interval there was a pious apprehension that they might become angry, leave the body and cause relatives serious troubles. It was to prevent these body spirits from getting at large before the end of the purification ceremonies (and perhaps also to prevent the body decaying) that the little jade objects were employed: the eyes and the mouth were covered with the tiny crickets, while the small cylinders were used to plug the body's natural openings. Besides, in a predominantly agricultural civilisation the cricket as a symbol of summer, and hence of ripening crops, must have possessed a mythical-religious significance, which explains the representation of the tiny insect all through the ages in innumerable decorative patterns.

Jade statuettes representing persons or animals are extremely rare before the Christian era. A figure of a crouching man—at present in a Chinese collection—is the only example of a carved human figure found in a Shang tomb. But in actual fact it has been carved out of a soft stone; similarly, the famous white tiger (also from the Shang period), mentioned in various records and in some of them described as jade, is made of a sort of marble. Both these art works were excavated in the Anyang zone, and therefore their origin can be pinpointed to the period between the 14th and 12th centuries BC.

A figure from the former Eumorfopoulos Collection (now in the British Museum), in green-grey nephritic jade with black and brown streaks, is usually accepted as dating back to the Chou period. Its attire, however, is characteristic of the first Han period, and personally I am convinced that its origin is not earlier than the 3rd to 2nd centuries BC.

From the same period, or a little later, came various water buffaloes (pre-eminently a beast of burden in the fertile Chinese plains) carved in the round out of blocks of jade. It is pretty obvious that jade carvers were as a rule inclined to represent animals in a lying position, with legs bent towards the belly, for the simple reason that with a particularly hard material the representation of a standing animal offered considerably greater difficulties. No reason, however, has been found to explain why in every case the head of the beast is turned outwards and its mouth half-open in a near-grin—as if they had been conceived by a contemporary Walt Disney.

The horse's head reproduced in this book (Plate 22), made of spotless green jade of excellent quality, belongs no doubt to the end of the Han period; that is, it cannot be earlier than the 2nd century AD. This conclusion is based on its bowed head and the fact that the figure—although stylised and carved in the round—lacks that vigour and fierceness which are characteristic of analogous sculptures discovered in tombs of the period between the 2nd century BC and the beginning of the first Christian century.

Until and all through the T'ang period (618-906) statuary in human form in jade appears practically non-existent, perhaps because of the splendid superiority of the art of clay-moulding. In fact jade sculpture could hardly compete with the perfect moulding and the subtlety of detail so much appreciated nowadays in ancient terracotta statuettes. Even so, there are various little reproductions of animals dating back to T'ang times, and they already reveal a remarkable sense of realistic proportions.

There is one everyday object that has played its part in the life of the average Chinese for 4000 years, and still does. It is his personal seal. It is no secret that until the comparatively recent past the vast majority of the Chinese were unable to write. Knowledge of their particularly difficult writing was confined to a small class of lettered men. As a result it was normal

44. Big tortoise. Ming period. British Museum, London.

45. Cicada-shaped pendant. Ming period. Museo Nazionale Orientale, Rome. Fiacchi-Gisondi Collection.

46.

that hardly requires special technical skill. In fact they can be engraved even on a material as hard as jade without the use of diamond or corundum tips.

There are two more typically Chinese objects which are nearly always made of jade: they are the 'Kuei' and the 'Ju I'.

The Kuei is an elongated tablet, never wider than about two inches, so that it can easily be held in the palm of the hand. It is at one and the same time a kind of baton of command and a sort of visiting card containing the name, functions and possibly the special merits of a person. To an artist his Kuei could be a present from the monarch in recognition of his high merits; to a court official called to service, a kind of Marshal's baton.

The Ju I is a strange kind of elegantly curved sceptre. It was used on solemn occasions (receptions, etc.) not only by the sovereign but also by dignitaries of great wealth. Seated, the gracious host would receive the compliments of his guests, clutching the Ju I in his right hand. Or, if he was a judge, he would pronounce verdicts in court in the same position. This sceptre was also used sometimes as a special gift, sent to somebody as a sign of respect and high esteem.

Plate 16 shows something of a curiosity—the design, copied from the original many years ago, of two strange objects which could easily be taken for two Kuei but are something completely different. The originals are not accessible, and it may be that the archaic characters are not very well drawn. The truth is that these ancient pieces were calcified and damaged to such an extent that the inscription was hardly visible at all.

Actually these two jades are possibly the proto-types of the very first passports. They are safe-conducts: one for river journeys, and one to tell the guards to admit the bearer to a not clearly specified city. I was told that they both dated back to the reign of Suen Wang of the Chou Dynasty (827-781 BC). Both are made of a brownish jade which is opaque and considerably decayed.

Such objects as cups and bowls made of jade are chronologically among the latest examples of Chinese carving art. This can be explained quite satisfactorily. It is easy to imagine what a hard task it must have been to cut a jade block in two halves and then to transform each into a bowl-shaped vessel without the help of modern rotary implements. The first such vessels, produced towards the end of the Chou period (if one is to believe the doubtful dates accepted by some museums), as well as those of the following centuries (throughout the T'ang period) are all thick-walled. Although many ancient poems extol the thinness of the wine goblets and tea cups made of genuine jade and used amidst the splendour of the Imperial court of the T'ang period, no such specimens have so far been discovered anywhere.

Actually, it is likely that in the descriptions of ancient ballads the fine clay cups ('Yüeh') from Cheking, with their grey-green or greenish-blue colour have been confused with genuine jade. So, for

49. Pendant in sounding-stone shape. Ch'ing period. Museo Nazionale Orientale, Rome. Fiacchi-Gisondi Collection.

50. Belt buckle. Ch'ing period. Museo Nazionale
Orientale, Rome. Fiacchi-Gisondi Collection.

54.   Small group of personages. Ch'ing period. Victoria and Albert Museum, London. W. H. Cape legacy. White nephritic jade. Minute little figures, sculptured all round, crowd round a bigger central figure, thus suggesting a movement towards the centre. 18th century.

55.   Sculptured panel: the Immortals in a retreat. Ch'ing period. Victoria and Albert Museum, London. Wells legacy. White jade. This panel was probably part of a piece of furniture or a small table screen. Attributed to the 18th century.

56.   Medallion or garment button. Ch'ing period (AD 1644-1911). Victoria and Albert Museum, London. Wells legacy. The relief sculpture represents a dragon among clouds. It probably belongs to the end of the 18th century, i.e. late Ch'ien Lung.

57.   Round jade medallion. Ch'ing period. Victoria and Albert Museum, London. The finely sculptured decoration covers the whole surface of the medallion and represents the Eight Immortals in the Taoist Empyrean, probably the Island of Happiness. On the reverse of the medallion there is a representation of Lao Tse (the Old Child). Reign of Ch'ien Lung (AD 1736-1795).

Imperial Palace, and it is even less likely that he was present at a banquet. He might have had his information from some palace official, who is likely to have embellished it in the habitual manner. Still, the essential particulars are confirmed in trustworthy records of the time.

It is obvious that the carving and engraving of objects of such size not only took years of hard work but also necessitated enormous quantities of abrasive. Thus it seems that the deposits of the precious 'black sand', extensively used by the Yüan, gave out somewhere around the beginning of the Ming period (AD 1368).

Books of the 15th and 16th centuries mention exclusively the 'red sand', that is, the powder made of pulverised garnets. Still, during the Ming period also, jade objects of considerable size were produced —although, as a rule, not in the shape of bowls and vases. The big tortoise in the British Museum (reproduced here in Plate 44) is about two feet long. If the dragon, incidentally, ranks highest as the symbol of royalty and of China herself, the tortoise follows closely in symbolic importance by reason of its shape. For the Chinese, the curved back represented the vault of Heaven and the flat belly the Earth. Thus the simple animal shape in a way symbolised the whole universe.

With the advent of the Ch'ing, the last of the Imperial Dynasties (1644-1911), jade-carving received a new and potent stimulus. Currently the quantities of nephrite arriving from Turkestan were increasing, and about the middle of the 18th century the imports of jadeite from Burma into China started, soon to be followed by the appearance of Siberian jade. Also new sources of corundum were discovered in Chinese territory, and the manufacture of the precious abrasive, as well as the technique of its utilisation, was perfected.

Instead of using pure corundum powder on a basis

of grease, Chinese lapidaries began to experiment with various mixtures of which each family jealously guarded the secret. As a rule they consisted in a combination of corundum and very fine clay, with possible additions of quartz and garnets, which were always ground to an exceedingly fine texture. These compounds, in use up to this day, require only the addition of some water to form a semi-liquid batter.

This new method had several advantages. In the first place, it offered the possibility of using an unskilled servant, or even a child, in the working process. Such a person had only to drop the abrasive in a continuous trickle from a bowl held above the surface being worked. At the same time this reduced the heat produced by the friction of the carving process. Moreover, the use of a newly invented big saw for cutting large blocks became possible, whereas the old-fashioned iron disc could never be made in a large size. This new tool, called by the Chinese a 'four-band saw', consisted originally of a fine iron wire kept taut by a robust bow. Two workmen seated on two sides of the boulder sawed, maintaining a regular see-saw motion, while a third made the abrasive mixture drip from above; it was collected in a basin underneath and kept for repeated use. This system eliminated also the fumes and odours of over-heated grease which had been caused by friction.

Among experts the assertion is common that the golden age of jade-carving was in the 18th century, during the reign of the Emperor Ch'ien Lung (1736-1795). I do not entirely agree with such statements.

yet the wide range of pantheistic jade statuettes deriving from this religion dates back only to the 13th century. Very popular indeed in the West are the elegant feminine statuettes generally known under the Chinese name of 'Kuan Yin'. Very few people, however, are aware of the fact that in reality they represent the asexual reincarnation of the Future Buddha Avalokitesvara (i.e. the Compassionate).

In China this Bodhisattva assumed its indubitably feminine aspect at the beginning of the T'ang period (AD 618) and was then worshipped as a benevolent goddess, protectress of the crops and of women in labour. The Jesuits in their wisdom tried to integrate this Kuan Yin cult with that of the Madonna. As a result, the representation of this original Bodhisattva appears after AD 1700 frequently transformed into a statuette of a gracious female with a child in her arms, though more often in ceramic than in jade. Statuettes representing other Bodhisattvas are also comparatively common, for example Manjusri seated on a lion, and Samantabhadra riding an elephant. And for the Tao cult believers there were, of course, figures of Lao Tz'u and his Eight Immortals in the first place, plus all the symbolic animals associated with them, the bat, the stork and the gazelle, to mention but the most important.

In the 17th century snuff became popular in China, and consequently, 'snuff bottles' appeared—tiny jade flagons (usually oval) or flagons with a jade stopper equipped with a tiny spoon with which to scoop out the small quantities of pulverised tobacco as required.

There was practically no citizen in the capital who would not have at least a decorative jade button adorning his dress or hat. Wealthy people had richly engraved belt buckles made of jade or ornaments for the hair—which were not confined to the fair sex. Table accessories in jade were popular with artists and men of letters: a cylinder for paint brushes, for instance, and brush supports on which to leave the writing brush momentarily while meditating. Further examples include little shades designed to reduce the glare of strong light and receptacles in which to dilute ink, which was made from tablets of hardened soot.

Very special sculptured representations that enjoyed great favour at the court of the Emperor Ch'ien Lung are known as 'jade mountains', and during his reign they could be seen almost everywhere in his vast palace. Some of these remarkable pieces weighed several hundred pounds. The monarch, himself an eminent artist and writer, took great pleasure in composing poems and writing them down with the paint brush; later they would be engraved with a diamond tip on the walls of these 'mountains' in an artful facsimile of his own handwriting. In fact, there are lines in these poems containing such sentiments as 'These words I have engraved on this exquisite, shining wall...'

These 'mountains' are clearly inspired by the Tao cult; they represent famous summits, particularly the K'un Lun, associated with this religion. (This in spite of the fact that the official religion was in essence Buddhist. For to Chinese people religion has always been something abstract and vague; in some cere-monies both monks of the Buddha and the Tao cult took part, performing the rites separately, each according to his creed.)

Generally speaking, these 'mountains' consist of huge monolithic boulders, with several peaks jutting out which are supposed to be the summits of a moun-tain chain. From the side walls little grottoes or shrines are carved out, peopled by human figures which represent the Immortals. The etymology of their Chinese name 'Hsien' is based on the two characters: 'Shan' (mountain) and 'Jen' (man).

Finally, thin jade slabs were used by the Chinese as a musical instrument. In place of bell-towers, which have never been known in China, many temples used to have slabs of jade hanging on cords and func-tioning as chimes. Striking them rhythmically in turn, a temple servant produced subdued and melodious sounds. Sometimes smaller and thinner pieces of jade were strung up on the outside of a temple, hanging on parallel strings very near to each other. The sligh-test puff of wind would make them tinkle and vibrate, producing sweet music.

In 1911 (with the advent of the Republic), or per-haps a little later, electric motors for the lathes reached China together with modern tools and car-borundum grindstones. Thus, jade carving changed from an intricate art requiring infinite patience and skill into a fairly unexciting handicraft. Even for a layman it is not too difficult to tell the difference be-tween an ancient jade piece and a modern one. The mechanically driven grindstones with their high abrasive potential produce clear and hard-cutting surfaces which were impossible to attain with the ancient methods. What is even more important, the nephritic jade polished with modern high-speed rotating discs presents a coldly smooth surface but lacks the exquisitely subdued shine of the ancient pieces.

Moreover, whenever mechanical methods replace manual work, the stamp of human personality disappears, together with all those tiny imperfections which endow the finished work with vibrant life. There is no longer any trace of the alert mind that inspires the hand with the passionate urge to create beauty . . . The work itself may be more perfect, it is true, but it will always have a certain coldness; it no longer speaks straight to the heart.

JADE IN PRE-COLUMBIAN AMERICA

In the vast area that encompasses the southern part of North America, Central America and the northern part of South America many civilisations succeeded each other over the ages and superimposed their characteristics on each other. For the sake of simplicity and because of ethnic and artistic analogies I propose to use the term 'Central America' for the whole area which surrounds the Gulf of Mexico. The area of the Maya culture extends from Mexico to the Yucatan Peninsula. The beginnings of this civilisation probably date back to the 3rd millennium, but no archaeological evidence whatsoever is available from that period. The first historical document which can be dated with certainty is an engraved slab of nephritic jade of the 2nd century AD. From that time onwards the Maya began erecting a commemorative stele every twenty years.

A marvellous funeral mask is exhibited in the Mexico City Museum. Made of jade, it has powerfully sculptured features of exceptional expressive force. It was found in a crypt near the village of S. Domingo, in the Mexican state of Chiapas, and can be pinpointed to the 5th or 6th century AD, which is the golden age of Maya art.

Strangely enough, after another three or four centuries this civilisation seems to have worn itself out. The reasons for this loss of strength seem all the more inexplicable as today there are still several million people who must be the direct descendants of the Maya. Of course, most of them exist in utterly miserable conditions.

In the Gulf of Mexico three main civilisations have succeeded each other, the first of them—Olmec—being by far the most important. Archaeology has given us the fullest evidence of an impressive jade-carving art which flourished there between the 5th and the 1st centuries BC. The raw material used is not actually genuine nephrite in most cases, but jadeite. Although the workmanship of these jade carvers never reached the heights of contemporary Chinese artistry, it shows unusual skill combined

63.

63.   Breast-plate worn at ritual ceremonies. Zapotec civilisation (3rd-2nd century BC). Museo Nacional de Antropología, Mexico City. This represents the mask of a God, and was used by Shaman priests of a particular type. The two holes at the sides are meant for a cord with which to hang the breast-plate round the neck.

64.   Statuette of a seated man. Maya art. Museo Nacional de Antropología, Mexico City. Nephritic jade. This figure, probably representing a wise man (or at any rate an important personage), possesses all the characteristics of the best Maya sculptures. 14th-15th century AD.

65.   Statuette of weeping child, sculptured all round. Olmeca art. Museo Nacional de Antropología, Mexico City. Green jadeite pebble. Despite its intentional classical simplicity it provides an excellent example of the expressive power so typical of Olmec art (3rd-1st century BC).

66.   Human mask in mosaic made of jade fragments. Maya art. Museo Nacional de Antropología, Mexico City. Because of its remarkable expressive power and the originality of its overall conception this mask is a classical sample of the Maya art of the 14th and 15th centuries AD.

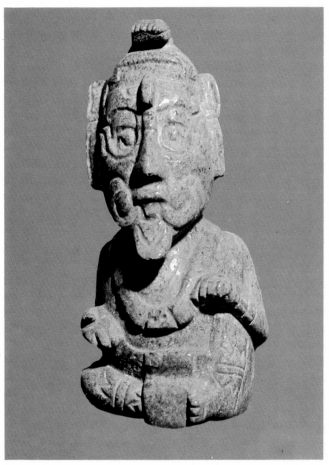

64. Statuette of seated man. Maya art. Museo Nacional de Antropología, Mexico City.

65. Statuette of weeping child, sculptured all round. Olmec art. Museo Nacional de Antropología, Mexico City.

66. Human mask in mosaic made of jade fragments. Maya art.
Museo Nacional de Antropología, Mexico City.

with remarkable artistic sensitivity. This deeply human sensitivity derived partly, perhaps, from the fact that all the work was done by hand, without any knowledge of iron and without the help of any of the ingenious rotary tools invented by the Chinese. The only metals known then were gold and copper. Obviously, the former was too soft to be suitable, and the second too scarce to be used by craftsmen. The only tools employed in shaping the jadeite were probably pieces of obsidian or volcanic lava. The objects excavated from the Maya's ancient dwellings or tombs are mostly statuettes and pendants representing humans, either erect or squatting. The oldest are carved in the round, with an accentuated stylisation of the features. In its peak period, however (3rd to 1st centuries BC), Olmec art presents also details of almost anatomical exactitude.

In the northern region of Vera Cruz a Totonac civilisation developed between the 4th and the 10th centuries AD. Their gem cutting art was of a high standard, but among the excavations jade objects are rather scarce. Those found might not even have been produced locally, and the raw material must at any rate have been imported. The minerals mainly used were diorite and various types of soft marble.

The Huastec civilisation came into being to the north of the preceding Totonac. It has left vestiges of a well developed art of clay moulding and characteristic pottery, but the gem cutting art is hardly worth mentioning.

On the Mexican plateau various civilisations

followed each other after the Neolithic Age, but little is known about them, and they left hardly any artistic heritage. Towards the beginning of the Christian era, however, a civilisation appeared which was to flourish for ten centuries and has left a great number of imperishable works of art.

It is somewhat strange that the original name of the people responsible for this civilisation is not known to us. Historically the name Teotihuacán is accepted, but it is fairly certain that this is the name given by the Aztecs to an important city situated where the great Sun Pyramid stands, this colossal structure having been built towards the middle of the 1st millennium by the original inhabitants of the region called Teotihuacán. It is beyond the scope of this work to deal with this superb monument and the artistic activities of its builders. It is, however, worth mentioning that they excelled in one form of art: their funeral masks, carved in jade or porphyry, are remarkably naturalistic and expressive.

In the 10th century this race was overcome by the Toltec, and the following period is to a certain extent characterised by the ornamental motifs preponderant in jade sculpture. Human form gives way to shapes inspired by the animal kingdom: mostly jaguars and winged serpents.

The Aztec descended from the north towards the end of the 13th or the beginning of the 14th century; then their penetration of the Mexican tableland commenced. In about 1330 they founded their capital, Tenochtitlan, where Mexico City stands today.

They swiftly came to dominate all the neighbouring tribes towards whom, however, they displayed great tolerance: instead of destroying the defeated, they rather absorbed them. This mixture of races and cultures gave rise to a magnificent civilisation which unfortunately lasted only about two centuries before being destroyed by Cortez and his followers.

Aztec jade carving art derives directly from the art of the Toltec and Olmec. Statuettes of deities, sculptured in jadeite, are frequent. They mostly look solemn and hieratic, and their identity is often obscure. Representations of the jaguar and the winged or feathered serpent, typical of the Toltec art, occur again in the same style.

This feathered serpent is obviously of totemistic origin. It was at first simply a stylised symbol but became in course of time the very emblem of a powerful deity. The feathers with which it is adorned must be considered a royal attribute. This reverential cult may be partly due to the abundance of deadly snakes in the region concerned, but there is another possible reason. Only the sovereign or the High Priest could decree death. Therefore beasts like the jaguar or the snake—which could kill without the slightest warning—became the object of reverence.

The animal representations engraved or sculptured in jade by Aztec artists are of exceptional naturalistic artistry. Skulls, either single or in chains, are also a frequently used ornamental motif, which is not surprising in view of the practice of propitiatory human sacrifices.

Interesting jadeite statuettes or pendants inspired by the human form have also been found in Costa Rica, but their symbolic significance more often than not escapes our understanding and becomes an object of controversy. Their style mostly bears the mark of a hieratic stylisation which possesses an individual and strange fascination.

Some descendants of the original population still exist in the northern region of the Amazon River, in glades carved out of impenetrable and awesome forest; their ancestors took refuge there from the onslaught of Brazil's Portuguese conquerors. There are only a few tribes — the Chavante, the Jivaro, etc. — counting now no more than several thousand people, whose development is still in the Paleolithic phase. Protected by the natural hazards of their forbidding surroundings, they avoid any contact with the outside world. Thus the limited information available concerning their existence and customs can generally be gleaned only from the few brave missionaries who withstand the perils of a deadly climate and live totally isolated in this enormous area several times the size of Great Britain.

Some years ago in Rio de Janeiro I received for the first time information about the jade amulets worn by some tribes of Indians. It was an Italian missionary, on his way back home after ten years in Equatorial Amazonia, who told me that he saw one of these amulets attached to a string and hanging round the neck of a Jivaro chief. He described it as a small green pebble, coarsely shaped like a human head and with-

67. Erect human figure. Olmec art. Museum für Völkerkunde,
Vienna.

67.   Erect human figure. Olmec art. Museum für Völkerkunde, Vienna. Green jadeite stone. Despite the mutilations suffered (both arms and one leg), the figure's well-preserved face reflects the high artistic level reached by Olmec art in the period between the 5th and the 3rd centuries BC, the period from which this work originates.

68.   Statuette of 'dragon', sculptured all round. Ancient Olmec art (8th-5th centuries BC). American Museum of Natural History, New York. Green jadeite with yellow specks. Dragon or another mythological animal sculptured out of a single jadeite block.

69.   Human figure sculptured out of a jadeite stone. Mixtec art. Nationalmuseet, Copenhagen. Specimen found in Mitla, a religious centre of the Zapotec (like Monte Alban), later conquered by the Mixtec who settled there.

70.   Sculptured plaque representing a deity. Maya art. American Museum of Natural History, New York. Probably from a region of Mexico, and not from Yucatan, the cradle of the Maya civilisation (4th-6th centuries AD).

71.   Hei-tiki amulet. Maori art. Museo Pigorini, Rome. Coarsely carved out of a nephritic jade pebble. A strange pendant-amulet. The eyes have been made more prominent by circles of red lacquer. Belongs probably to the period between the 16th and 17th centuries AD.

68.

69. Human figure sculptured out of a jadeite
stone. Mixtec art. Nationalmuseet, Copenhagen.

70. Sculptured plaque representing a deity. Maya art.
American Museum of Natural History, New York.

out any artistic pretensions. Having acted as a doctor and cured this chief when he was gravely ill, the missionary had been on particularly friendly terms with him. Despite this, an attempt to acquire the amulet in question caused considerable animosity, which persisted for some time and was only dispelled with difficulty.

As things are—with one-third of the Amazon area still unexplored territory—it is impossible to ascertain whether there exist any alluvial deposits of jade or jadeite there. There are, it is true, some adventurers who in defiance of all perils search for precious stones in the riverbeds of those innumerable 'igarapés' (small rivulets with changeable courses) which form an inextricable maze in the midst of the equatorial forests. But they, even if the expedition has been successful, are hardly inclined to reveal details of their activities for fear of taxes and official interference. (Brazil is the second greatest diamond producing country in the world, but according to government estimates 98 per cent of these precious stones are simply smuggled out of Brazil.)

It is also conceivable that any jade pieces found in the Amazon region (and there are only vague reports of their existence) are actually of Costa-Rican origin. The only fact that supports my belief in their existence is the missionary's description of the unique amulet owned by the Jivaro chief.

This provokes another speculation. The tribe is known for its custom of keeping the mummified heads of their defeated enemies. It is a special art to

71. Hei-tiki amulet. Maori art. Museo Pigorini, Rome.

crush the cranial bones of the severed head in such a way as to leave the skin unscathed, to extract the bone fragments and to fumigate the skull until it is reduced to the size of a fist—so that it can be then hung up as a trophy. This peculiar and savage custom suggests a certain connection between these trophies and the shape of that Jivaro amulet—provided that it was in fact produced locally. This, however, remains my personal theory, without concrete proofs. One can rely only on conjectures, and sum up the subject only by stating that the technique of jade carving in Central America must have borne great similarity to that of Stone Age China.

JADE CARVING IN NEW ZEALAND

The native population inhabiting the two South Pacific islands known as New Zealand are the Maoris, and there seems no doubt that their first habitations were on the North Island. They must have settled there around AD 1000, and created a characteristic civilisation of their own which is now being revealed by archaeological finds. It is, however, a complete mystery how they came to discover the rich alluvial deposits of nephritic jade, situated exclusively in the western region of the other, southern island. Jade is found there in the shape of fairly big pebbles, in two valleys protected by a towering mountain chain which could almost be called impassable. This region still is called 'the Green Country' or 'Jade Country'.

The trip of the Maori sailors in their fragile canoes across the stretch of stormy ocean to the South Island must have been long and perilous. It was made several centuries after their first landing on the North Island: in the more ancient layers of their excavations archaeologists have found only remnants of objects made of bone or ivory, but no jade whatsoever.

As a matter of fact, jade partly revolutionised the customs and habits of this race. While other civilisations used this stone to satisfy their urge for ornamental luxury, the Maoris turned it to more utilitarian purposes, making knives, hatchets and other tools, albeit primitive. These served their basic needs, enabling them to improve the quality of their woodwork as well as to build houses and canoes which they lovingly decorated with intricate carvings and totemistic ornaments.

Although New Zealand became an English colony in 1769, when Captain Cook took possession of the land on behalf of the British Crown, until about 150 years ago the Maoris led a Stone Age existence.

As they had no metals, the carving of jade (which in Maori language is known as 'pounamu') must have been a difficult task. It must be assumed that for this purpose they used sharp-edged pieces of jade itself, employing also in the process wetted quartz-containing sand which abounds on New Zealand beaches. At first the Maoris confined themselves to transporting the valuable stones to their home on the North Island, and working them there. To obtain them they would actually organise warlike expeditions to the

South Island. Only later, it seems, did they occupy the other island too and arrange to work the jade where it was found. Still, the best of the ancient jade articles have been found on the North Island.

There is no indication that the belief in jade's medicinal virtues so common in China ever took root among the Maoris. The almost reverential treatment of this mineral and the high value attached to it arose from the risks involved in obtaining it, as well as from its extreme hardness and the utility of the implements made with it.

Thus the very knives, hooks and other jade implements became the first adornments of the Maoris— worn on a string around the neck or attached to the bow of a canoe as talismans to ensure a good catch, since fish was the Maoris' staple food.

Among the ancient objects of the Maori civilisation there are two characteristic articles worthy of note. The 'mere' was a sort of mace or combat bludgeon which was at the same time the emblem of the chief and the symbol of authority. The 'hei-tiki' (cf. Plate 71), on the other hand, is a curious flat pendant whose shape was perhaps suggested by the hatchet. It is usually not longer than $2\frac{1}{2}$ to 3 inches and represents a strangely contorted human figure, apparently so shaped as to fit into a rectangle. The disproportionately large head is inclined to one side and rests directly on the shoulders without any neck, whilst the legs are contracted and connected to an arc which supports the body. There is also a coarsely engraved spiral-inspired decoration.

The symbolic significance of the hei-tiki is somewhat obscure. It is said to be a talisman and a representation of fecundity; on the other hand it also plays a part in certain funeral rites. In a certain sense it is an object of veneration similar to the ancestral tablets of the Chinese. At the death of a family head, his hei-tiki was buried with him. After the passing of a fixed period it was disinterred and then became an object of even more profound worship. Friends of the deceased gathered, formed a circle around the hei-tiki, and then intoned chants and funeral dirges.

The greatest technical problem for the ancient Maoris was always how to perforate a jade object so as to be able to append it. Some assert that they used for the purpose the same kind of primitive wooden drill as the ancient Chinese—that is, a wooden stick (instead of bamboo, which was not available) rotated with the help of a coiled cord drawn by a bow. It seems improbable, however, that they had such a contraption. A close scrutiny of the holes made in ancient Maori jade pieces clearly shows the obvious irregularities of their shape and leads to the conclusion that they were made by hand, very slowly, probably with the help of a pointed jade splinter and wet sand.

Today, in New Zealand as in China, jade is worked with carborundum drills and electrically propelled grindstones. Although the Chinese products are superior, the modern jade articles of New Zealand origin have their market and are very much in demand.

LIST OF ILLUSTRATIONS Page

157